Annie Mouse's Route 66 A

A Photo Journal

Fifth in the Adventures of Annie Mouse Series

Written by: Anne Maro Slanina, Ph.D.
and
Illustrated by: Kelsey Collins

It was the last day of the school year and I couldn't wait to get home! Mommy and Daddy had said there would be a big surprise for us when we got home from school. I was so excited that I ran ahead of the others.

As I got closer to home, I saw Daddy's old car loaded up with suitcases. I wondered if we were going to move! I DID NOT WANT TO MOVE!

I ran into the house to ask Mommy and Daddy what was going on! I saw them looking over a big map that was spread out on the floor.

Daddy called us all together and told us we would be going to California to visit Mommy's relatives. Along the way, we would explore Route 66 and even visit the Grand Canyon! We didn't know anything about Route 66. Daddy pointed to the red line on the map and explained that it was the first paved route to go all the way across the country. Big Brother Bobby was eager to start looking at Mommy's travel guide. And I was going to be allowed to take my own pictures!

We left for our trip that night. Daddy and Mommy took turns driving all night long while we slept. Well, I TRIED to sleep, but I was so excited it was hard to sleep. I love adventures!

When we finally stopped we were at the Joliet, Illinois Historical Museum where we would begin to learn about Route 66. I couldn't wait to start taking pictures!

Joliet Area Historical Museum, Joliet, IL

Once inside, we sat on a bench that looked like the back seat of an old car and watched a movie that introduced us to Route 66. We learned that it starts north of Joliet in Chicago and was pieced together from lots of dirt trails and paths. It goes through eight states for more than 2,000 miles! Route 66 is sometimes called "The Mother Road" or "The Main Street of America." In the lobby was a statue of our country's 16th president, Abraham Lincoln, that would soon be moved to one of the street corners where Lincoln spoke. In the gift shop, Mommy bought a Route 66 Travel Guide for Kids.

Joliet Area Historical Museum, Joliet, IL

This drawbridge goes over the Des Plains River and can be seen from the Visitor's Center.

We saw so many interesting things as we continued our drive through Illinois!

In Wilmington, Daddy suddenly stopped the car in front of a very tall spaceman statue! Big Brother Bobby read from our guidebook, "The Gemini Giant is one of several statues known as "Muffler Men" because at one time statues like these were used to advertise automobile mufflers and tires." Now this one stands in front of The Launching Pad Diner.

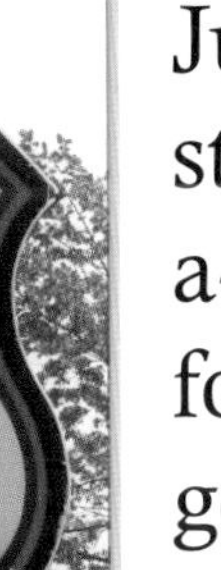

Just down the road, we stopped at The Polk-a-Dot Drive In Diner for lunch. Mommy and Daddy got excited when they saw the statues of some old movie stars alongside the building. While we waited for our lunch, we looked around at all of the fun stuff inside. My favorite was the juke box!

An old horse-drawn streetcar sat behind the Riviera Restaurant in Gardner. Just down the road, we got to walk inside a tiny jail!

By the time we got to Pontiac we learned that The Riviera Restaurant had been destroyed in a fire.

Sometimes the road would suddenly come to an end. Mommy read from her travel guide, "parts of Route 66 were destroyed when the interstate was built."

Pontiac had another museum and lots of pictures painted on the sides of buildings that Mommy called murals. This one was my favorite.

When we found the route again, we also found Funks Grove, where they make real maple "sirup." Mommy even bought some to take home with us. Back on the route, we found another "Muffler Man" statue in Atlanta. This one was holding a hot dog! Just down the street is a library with a really interesting shape. I wanted to go inside, but it was already closed for the day.

At the Historic Route 66 Visitors Center and Henry's Rabbit Ranch in Staunton, Rich Henry introduced us to his rabbit friends. He even let us pet Big Red! While Mommy shopped, Big Brother Bobby took this picture of Daddy and me. "Hare it is!"

Our last stop in Illinois was the Old Chain of Rocks Bridge. The bridge goes over the Mississippi River and connects Illinois and Missouri. Cars aren't allowed to go over it anymore, though. According to our guide book, the bridge has a bend in the middle. We wanted to walk across it and see the bend, but there was a flash flood warning and we had to leave quickly! I never saw so much rain come down at once!

The roads got a little confusing and Daddy ended up going in the wrong direction for a little bit so we landed in Collinsville, IL where we saw a water tower that looked like a catsup bottle!

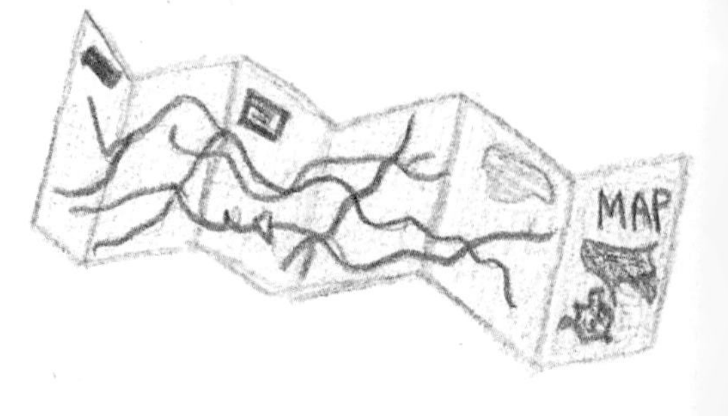

Finally, we were entering St. Louis, Missouri, which is known as the Gateway to the West. We all got really excited when we saw the Gateway Arch come into view. It looked so big! Our guide book said the arch is 630 feet tall and you could take a ride inside all the way to the top! Mommy was afraid to go that high, so we didn't get to go inside. Don't tell anyone, but I was glad!

Daddy said there would be a lot to do and see in Missouri. Our first stop was in Stanton at the Meramec Caverns. The tour was really interesting! We learned that saltpeter, which was used to make gunpowder, had been mined here a long time ago. I got to see REAL stalactites and stalagmites for the first time! We also learned that Jesse James, who robbed banks and trains a long time ago, used to hide out in these caverns.

When we arrived in Cuba, we saw right away why it is called the "Route 66 Mural City." There are amazing murals all over the town! Big Brother Bobby said that he hopes he can paint like that some day.

Outside the Fanning US 66 Outpost and General Store we felt really tiny next to a huge rocking chair that claimed to be the world's largest.

Mommy noticed a pretty stone arch with the words, "Trail of Tears." It looked beautiful, but it sounded like something sad. Big Brother Sam said he knew all about the Native American Trail of Tears. He said we would learn all about it in our Social Studies classes when we were older.

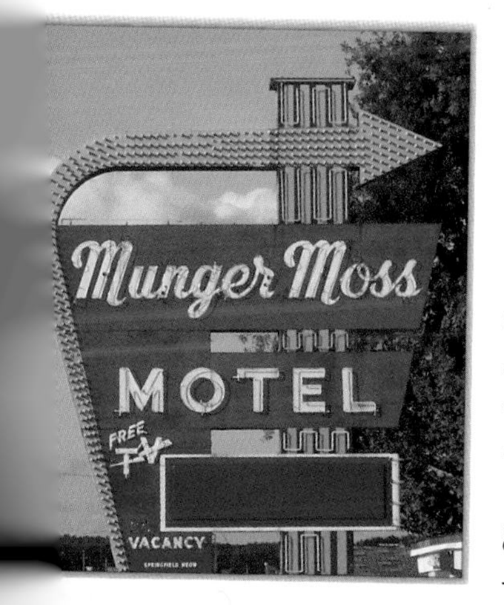

After another very long day driving, we stopped for the night at The Munger Moss Motel in Lebanon. I thought the motel office was a museum because it had lots of interesting stuff for us to look at. The owners laughed and told us that the real Missouri Route 66 Museum was in the ibrary not far away. Daddy said we'd check it out n the morning before getting back on the road. We vere glad we did! We even saw the original phones hat used to be in The Munger Moss!

At the Historic Route 66 Antique Mall in Phillipsburg, we saw many antiques. These old wagons were my favorites.

Daddy told us that when Missouri was first settled, people traveled in buggies and wagons like these.

Back on Route 66, the thumping of the tires as we drove through empty towns and lonely roads put me to sleep.

I didn't wake up again until the car stopped in front of Gary Turner's Gay Parita's Sinclair Station near Paris Springs. Gary invited us all into his garage where there was so much to see! We were there for a very long time, sipping our root beers and listening to Gary's stories. By the time we left we all felt like we'd made another new friend. When we left, Gary signed our travel book with, "Friends for life!"

On our way to Carthage, we thought we saw a little plane crashing into the bushes! Daddy slammed on the brakes and then we all laughed. Big Brother Sam read from our guide book: "The Flying Crap Duster is the name of a folk art sculpture made from an antique manure spreader by artist Lowell Davis." We giggled all the way to Carthage!

When we arrived in Carthage, Daddy parked the car and we walked around the town square. We learned that the big, beautiful building is the Jasper County Courthouse. We went inside to see the Route 66 Museum and a nice lady offered us a ride in an old-fashioned elevator. It looked like a cage. Mommy said all elevators used to be like this. It was fun!

Back in the car, we drove past the Carthage Route 66 Drive-In Theatre. Daddy said maybe we'd get to see a movie at a Drive-In one day.

Our last stop in Missouri was in Joplin. We drove past a school that had a really cool sign out front with a huge crayon and ruler. All of us kids got really excited when we saw a huge Ferris Wheel and we begged to stop at the amusement park! Mommy and Daddy agreed and I got to ride the carousel!

After a fun afternoon at the park, we searched for Woody's Wood-Fire Pizza because Mommy said her Cousin Bob had eaten there and recommended it. Cousin Bob was right, the pizza WAS yummy!

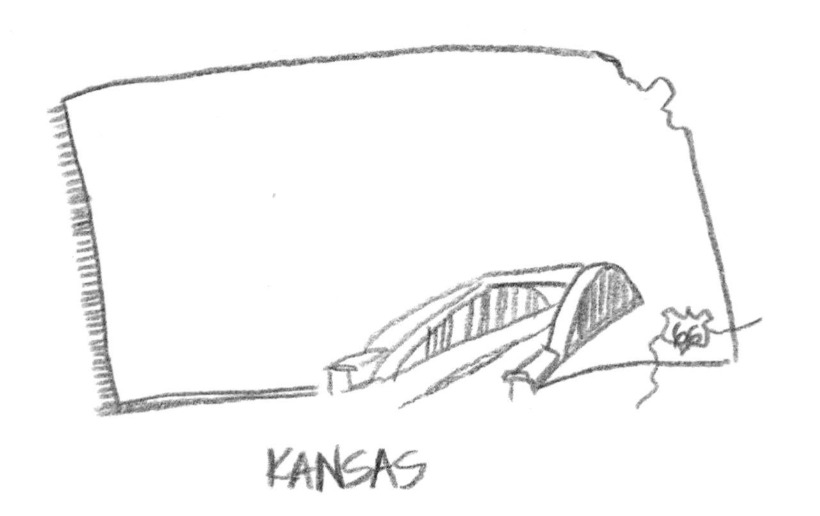

Our guide book said Kansas has only 13 miles of Route 66 so we wouldn't be in Kansas very long! Our first stop was in Galena, at a place called 4 WOMEN on the ROUTE. It used to be a gas station, but it is now a really cool gift shop and restaurant. Daddy and my brothers thought the old tow truck was the best of all.

The pretty flowers in front of The Eisler Brothers Market in Riverton caught Mommy's attention so we stopped there. We were surprised to find that it is much more than a food market; it is also a Route 66 gift shop. Mommy bought some cheese for us to snack on later.

Our next stop was the Marsh Rainbow Bridge. I thought it was going to be painted in the colors of the rainbow, but it was white. I got to take a picture of the Route 66 shield on the road. Big Sister Jenny read from the travel guide, "The bridge was designed by an engineer named James Marsh and built around 1923. It's called Rainbow Bridge because of its shape. This is the last Marsh Bridge on Route 66- all the others have been demolished."

BAXTER SPRINGS
CITY LIMIT

There was much more to see in Kansas than we thought! We stopped in Baxter Springs and walked up and down the street before stopping at the Café on the Route to have dinner. According to the sign on the building, Jesse James had been an uninvited guest in this building, too!

ROUTE 66 ROADSIDE ATTRACTION

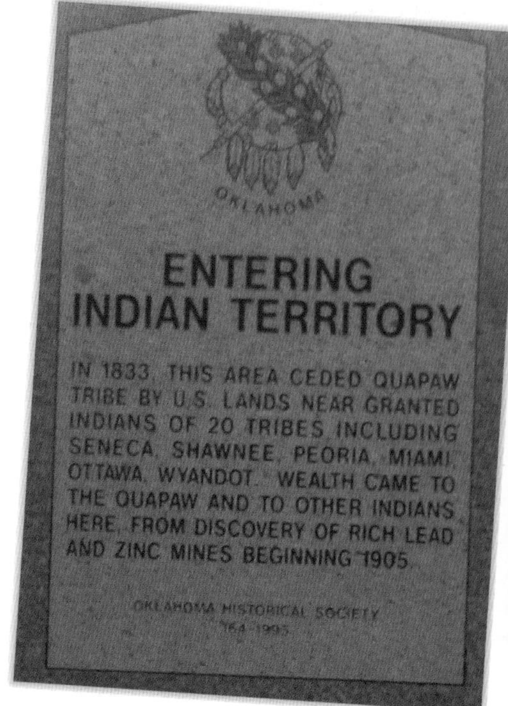

Before we knew it, we were in Oklahoma! In Quapaw a stone monument let us know that we were "Entering Indian Territory."

We stopped for ice cream cones in Commerce and learned that this town was the boyhood home of Mickey Mantle, the famous baseball player.

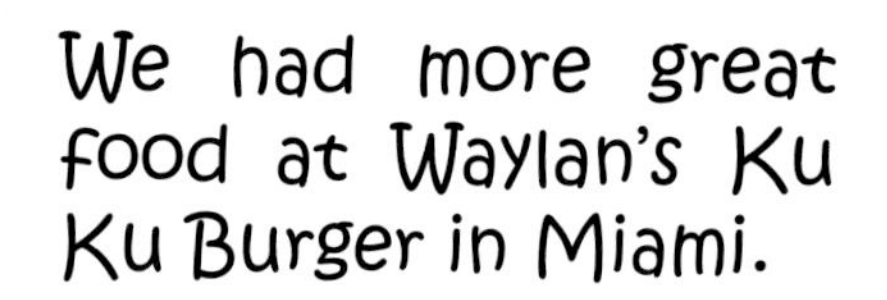

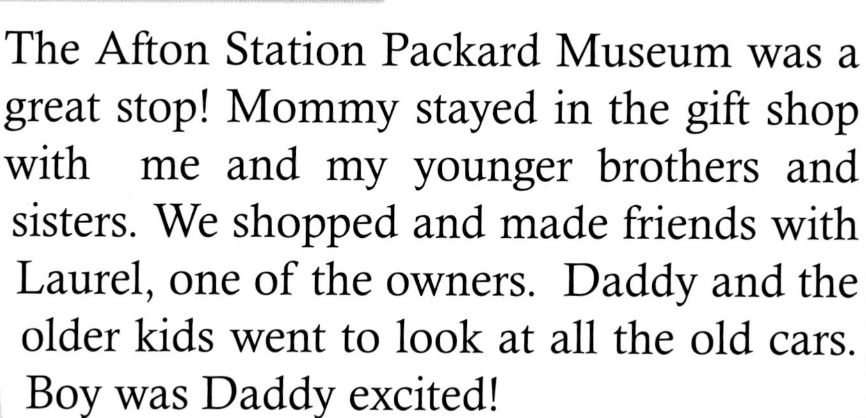

The Afton Station Packard Museum was a great stop! Mommy stayed in the gift shop with me and my younger brothers and sisters. We shopped and made friends with Laurel, one of the owners. Daddy and the older kids went to look at all the old cars. Boy was Daddy excited!

As we continued the drive on Route 66 there were many old buildings and cars that had been abandoned. I thought the stone buildings were beautiful and it made me sad to see them empty. Daddy said it made him sad to see all the old cars left sitting to rust.

We saw the World's Largest Totem Pole in Foyil at Ed Galloway's Totem Pole Park. It is 90 feet tall and Little Sister Sandy said she couldn't even see the top!

When we found the Blue Whale Swimming Park in Catoosa, we were all disappointed to discover that it was no longer open. It looked like it would have been a lot of fun!

We drove through Sapulpa, Bristow and Depew before finally stopping for dinner at Gar Wooly's in Davenport. Everyone was so friendly there; we left with smiles and full tummies!

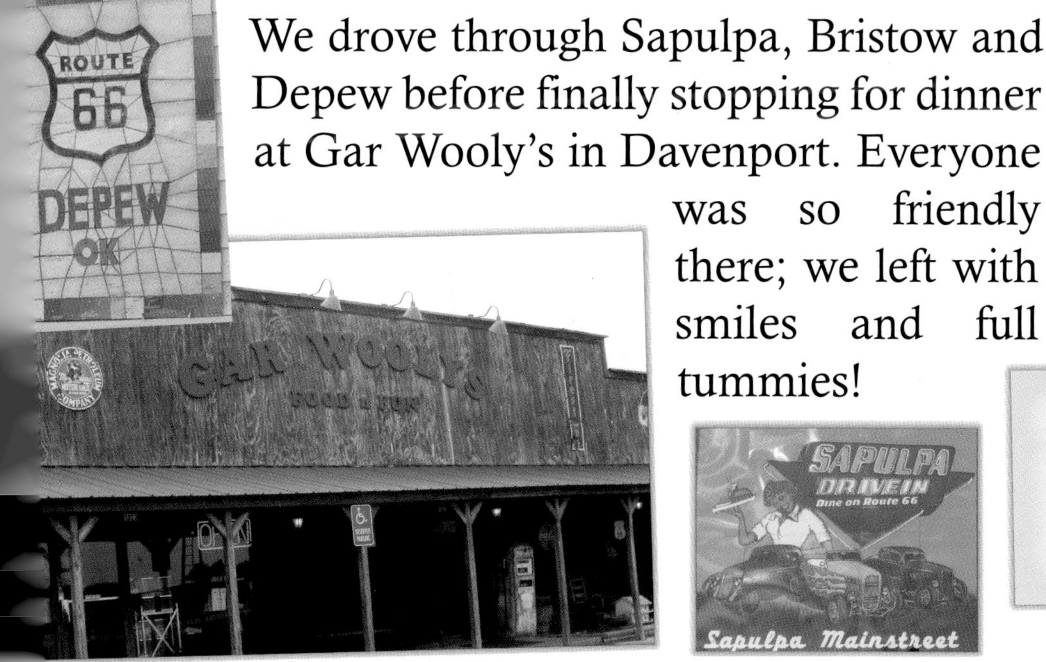

This huge plate, cup and bottle made an interesting display on a corner in Sapulpa.

Our guide book said the Seaba Station in Warwick was an antique store and Mommy really wanted to stop there, but it was all closed up. It had a restroom building beside it that Daddy called an "outhouse." We were all happy that we don't have one of those at our house!

In Wellston I took a picture of one of the murals. I love seeing the artwork on the sides of the buildings.

We spent a lot of time in Arcadia. Our first stop was John Hargrove's museum. It was really cool! It was filled with replicas of Route 66 landmarks. John even let me sit in the car that sticks out of the side of the building!

Mommy and Daddy both got excited when they saw the Round Barn of Arcadia come into view. They had both seen pictures of it in their travel guide and couldn't wait to see it. It was HUGE and we felt really tiny inside. We even got to go upstairs to see where they used to have barn dances. Mommy and Daddy even waltzed all the way around the barn once.

Further down the road was a store called POPS that had a HUGE bottle of pop outside. We learned that it was 66 feet high and changed colors at night. They sold all kinds of soda pop inside. I didn't know soda pop came in so many colors before!

As we drove through Oklahoma City, we saw a huge Braum's milk bottle sitting on top of a triangle-shaped building. We also saw many buildings that looked like giraffes! We learned from our guide book that these were built from "giraffe-styled Ozark sandstone."

At the Cherokee Trading Post in El Reno, we learned that we should look for special tags that are placed on all hand-crafted Native American items to be sure they are authentic. Mommy bought a Native American flute. It sounds really pretty when she plays it!

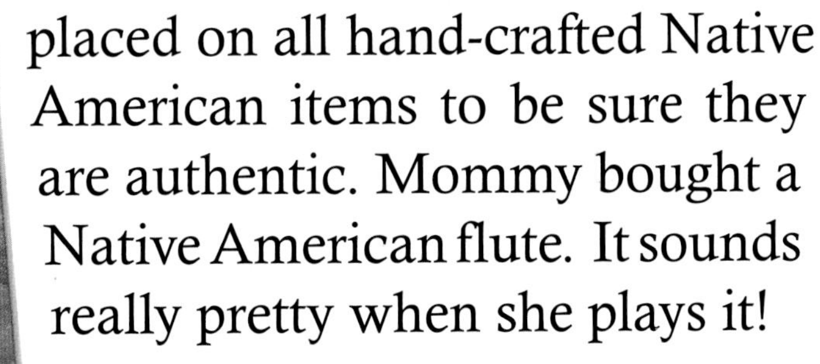

Just past Hydro, Daddy stopped the car in front of a gas station. "Lucille's" is no longer open for business, but is on display to show what it looked like a long time ago when Lucille and Carl Hamons owned it. Our guide book said that people who were traveling west to look for work would often run out of money or their cars would break down. Big Brother Bobby read from the guide book, "Lucille came to be known as 'The Mother of The Mother Road' because she helped everyone in need." It sounds like she was a nice lady.

A few miles down the road we came to Lucille's Roadhouse. It was built to look just like Lucille's gas station. We stopped to eat and got to sit at a counter and have yummy burgers and fries!

In Clinton we stopped at the Oklahoma Route 66 Museum.

There were so many cool displays to see inside the museum. We had a great time learning about what life was like before people could drive fast on the interstates. Mommy said back then people took time to enjoy their neighbors and no one was a stranger.

Daddy wanted to check out the diner beside the museum, but Mommy said we couldn't possibly eat anything else. Daddy laughed and told us that we couldn't eat there, only look, since it was part of the Route 66 Museum display. We learned it was called a "Valentine Diner," named for the man who started these small counter service diners.

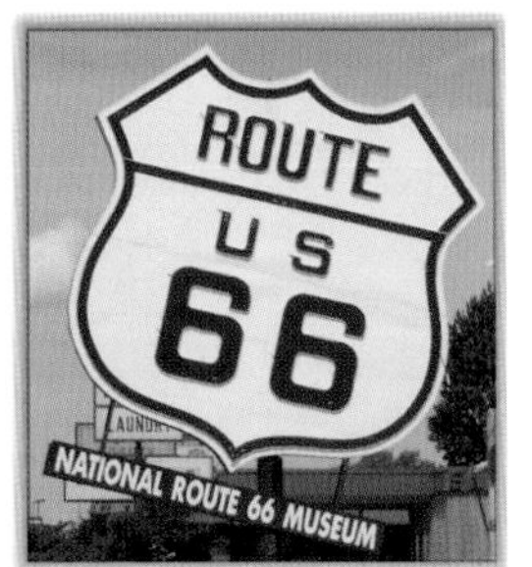

Elk City has a National Route 66 Museum with a 15 foot tall statue of a Kachina Doll out front and lots of buildings to explore inside and out!

There was so much to see here that we all started to run in different directions! I was rushing to go sit inside a car with a television screen to see and feel what traveling on the original Route 66 felt like when Mommy and Daddy had to remind us of the rules to stay together and NO RUNNING inside.

We saw three tiny jails in Oklahoma: one in Foss Park, another in Canute, and the third in Texola.

Our first stop in the Texas Panhandle was in Shamrock. A leprechaun welcomed us! Big Sister Jenny reminded me of the time I got lost searching for the leprechaun guarding a pot of gold at the end of the rainbow and everyone laughed.

At the Shamrock Chamber of Commerce building we picked up some Texas travel brochures. According to our travel guide, this building used to be an inn and café.

As we entered McLean we saw a RATTLESNAKES sign. We all felt a little scared! The Mouse Family wouldn't be stopping to see rattlesnakes!! Instead we stopped at the Devil's Rope Museum. None of us knew that "devil's rope" was another name for barbed wire until we visited this museum. We were amazed at all of the different sculptures made out of barbed wire! There was also a gift shop inside where Mommy bought some Route 66 playing cards and Daddy bought a little chunk of the original Texas Mother Road.

After we left the museum, we continued down the road and stopped to take pictures of a restored service station. Daddy said it reminded him of the gas station his own father owned when he was little.

Further down the road was a town called Alanreed. We stopped at the General Store and Post Office for some cold drinks. It had a tiny jail beside the building, too.

Back on Route 66, we came upon a water tower that seemed to be leaning! Our guide book said that it wasn't a real water tower; it was just built like that to advertise a truck stop.

We drove through Groom and found a small grocery store that reminded Mommy of one we have back home. We stopped the car and got out to buy some snacks. The people who worked there were very nice to all of us even though we were strangers in their town.

In Conway we saw Bug Ranch! There were cars sticking up out of the ground, like they had been planted there! There were paint cans on the ground around them. We couldn't believe we were allowed to paint whatever we wanted on the cars-- the tour book said that it was allowed! I grabbed a can and sprayed, "Annie Mouse" on one of the cars!

In Amarillo we stopped at The Big Texan for lunch. They offer a free 72 ounce steak, but only if you can eat it all! It was a fun place to eat and they let us keep the menus as souvenirs!

I couldn't believe my eyes when we came upon more cars that were planted in the ground! This was "Cadillac Ranch" and was in the middle of a pasture. We were a little nervous about painting on these cars since the cows seemed to be enjoying them. The cows on our farm are friendly, but I didn't know these cows! I asked Daddy if everybody in Texas plants their cars when they don't want them anymore! Mommy laughed and said that this was a form of art.

In Vega we saw boots hanging in the trees at Dot's Mini Museum!

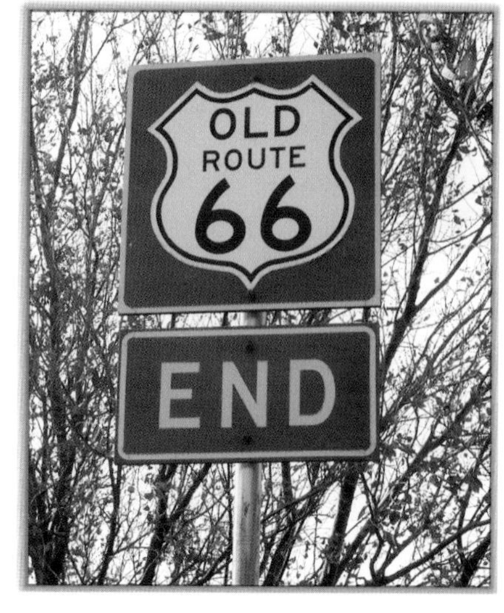

In Adrian, a sign let us know that we had already driven halfway through Route 66. The Midpoint Café was across the street from the sign. Big Brother Sam read from the guide book that they have 'ugly crust pies" and Mommy said we would have to stop and find out what THOSE were. It was really cool inside! The pie was pretty yummy, too!

The last town we went through in Texas was called Glenrio. Our guide book said it is a "ghost town." I didn't want to see any ghosts! The older kids laughed at me when I said this. Daddy explained that "ghost town" means that all of the people have left the town and buildings and cars are left abandoned.

Glenrio is also the first town in New Mexico. According to our guide book, "through the years, the route has changed in some areas." This was one of those areas and

our guide book listed two choices: The old dirt road option or the newer, paved route. Daddy chose to take the original "Dirt 66" road since the guide book said it was more scenic.

For many miles it seemed like we were driving through a pasture. We only saw abandoned buildings and cars, and even a "Modern Restrooms" building, but no people OR ghosts!

Finally we were in Tucumcari! There was so much to see that we spent the whole day! Many of the buildings had beautiful murals painted on them. I was so excited when we went into the dinosaur museum, that I left my camera in the car and didn't get to take any pictures. You'll have to stop and see it for yourself!

We all got tee shirts at Tepee Curios.

Sally squealed, "What's THAT?" as she pointed to a big Mexican hat on top of a restaurant called LaCita. Mommy said the hat is called a sombrero.

Mommy shopped inside Timeless Treasure while us kids stayed outside with Daddy and I took more pictures.

TIMELESS TREASURE

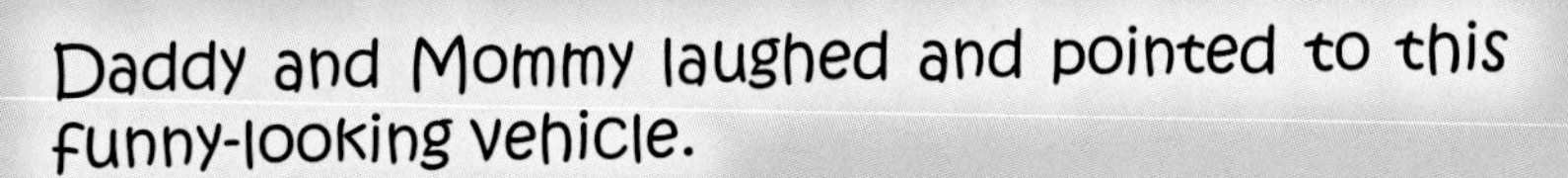
Daddy and Mommy laughed and pointed to this funny-looking vehicle.

There were really cool signs everywhere! We saw a camel on a sign for the Motel Safari and learned from our guide book that camels had once roamed this area! They had been brought in during the 1800s to carry supplies for the surveyors who were trying to map out roadways in the area.

Mommy and Daddy had a hard time deciding which motel to stay in for the night; there were so many great ones to choose from!

Blue Swallow
MOTEL
TV

Just when we thought we had seen everything Tucumcari had to offer, we saw this Route 66 sculpture as we were heading out of town.

After leaving Tucumcari, we drove through more ghost towns. Newkirk and Cuervo had lots of empty businesses, churches, schools and homes.

In Santa Rosa, we stopped at the Route 66 Auto Museum where I took this picture of an old car sitting high up on a pole! I also found a sign for "snake oil" but none of us wanted to try any! We stopped at the Blue Hole and watched people swim in special diving suits. Daddy said the water temperature was too cold to swim in without the special suits.

We were all surprised when this animal ran across the road in front of our car. Daddy thought it was a moose and Mommy thought it was a deer. We'd never seen anything quite like it before!

This sign welcomed us to the small town of Moriarty.

I had never seen colorful, rocky mountains like this before!

In Albuquerque there were so many diners to choose from and we all wanted to stop someplace different. We finally decided to get hot dogs at The Dog House and milkshakes at the 66 Diner. No one was disappointed!

Mommy pointed out that many signs had balls and stars on them. Our guide book said that this is known as "Googie style" architecture, which was popular in the 1950s. Many signs for businesses use this style.

Mommy wanted to shop in Olde Towne Albuquerque. This was the first time any of us had ever seen an adobe building before. According to our guide book, "Adobe buildings are built from mud bricks."

OLD ACOMA
"SKY CITY"

Legend describes Acoma as a "place that always was". Archeological evidence shows it has been occupied since at least the 13th century. Established on this mesa for defensive purposes, Acoma was settled by inhabitants of nearby pueblos which had been abandoned. Nearly destroyed by the spanish in 1599, Acoma was quickly reestablished by ancestors of its present occupants.

Big Brother Sam asked to stop to read this sign about "Sky City." We found the information on the sign interesting enough to decide to see the city. It was amazing to see the old city and the way the people live without modern conveniences. I wasn't allowed to take pictures because a special permit is required.

An old covered wagon showed us the point of The Continental Divide. The guide book said this is where "rainfall drains to the west into the Pacific Ocean and to the east, into the Atlantic Ocean." Beside the wagon is a hogan, a traditional Navajo dwelling, and we got to look inside.

A HUGE, colorful pot welcomed us to Gallup! In all of the shops we saw turquoise stones in jewelry, on pottery, and even on musical instruments. We made new friends in Ray's Trading Company, where we learned all about the different types and colors of turquoise and the artistry that goes into making the beautiful jewelry. Daddy let each of us pick out a small, carved animal. I got a tiny beaver with tiny blue stones for eyes. I learned that this was called a Native American fetish or good-luck symbol. I learned that each animal has a special meaning and my beaver is a symbol of a builder-- perfect for me since I like to make things!

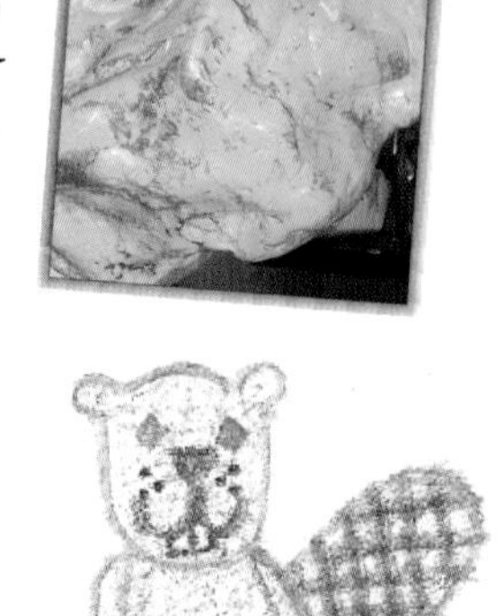

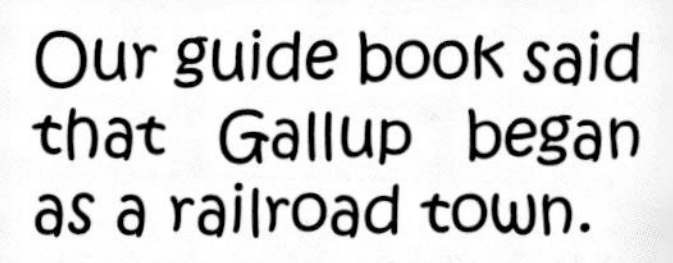

Our guide book said that Gallup began as a railroad town.

We stopped for the night at the El Rancho Motel. The sign said it was the "home of the movie stars!" It was really cool inside! All of the doors had names of famous old-time movie stars on them.

We all cheered as we crossed into Arizona! There were many Indian Trading Posts selling Native American made blankets, pottery and jewelry.

When we saw dinosaurs and teepees along the roadside, we begged Daddy to stop so we could explore. At Stewart's Rock Shop we saw not only rocks and dinosaurs, but live ostriches, too! There were lots of cool things for us kids to look at here.

Across the road, at the Painted Desert Indian Center, we learned how horse hair pottery is made. We helped Mommy pick out a beautiful vase to take to cousins Mary and Bob.

When we got to Holbrook, we saw a motel where you could stay in a wigwam for the night.

We had lunch at Joe & Aggies Cafe, then stopped in the Navajo County Museum to learn about the area.

An entrance into the Petrified Forest National Park is in Holbrook. We drove through the park and were amazed to see the huge, colorful rocks. We learned that it is against the law to take anything, including rocks, out of a National Park. We stayed in the car as Daddy drove through the park. It was so hot, none of us wanted to get out and walk around!

PONY EXPRESS

Annie Mouse
P.O. Box 142
Harrisville, PA 16038

A sign told us that Holbrook is home to the Hashknife Pony Express. A long time ago mail used to be delivered by men riding horses. Our guide book said that Pony Express riders still deliver the mail from Holbrook to Scottsdale once a year as a special celebration. We learned that you could mail yourself a letter and have it postmarked by the Pony Express. I'm going to do that when we get home!

Jack Rabbit Trading Post used with permission

In Joseph City, we stopped at the Jack Rabbit Trading Post where Daddy bought himself a new coffee mug and I had my picture taken with the Jack Rabbit!

Jack Rabbit Trading Post used with permission

On our way to Winslow, suddenly the sky turned brown and the wind was pushing our car back and forth. Daddy couldn't see where he was driving and had to pull over until the dust storm died down. It was really scary! It looked like a brown blizzard!

In Winslow we got out to take a picture with the statue of the man "Standin' on the Corner." Mommy and Daddy started to sing, "Standin' on a corner in Winslow, Arizona..." when they saw this statue. We also saw a huge Route 66 shield painted on the intersection of the road. The La Posada Hotel was just down the street. Our guide book said a woman, Mary Colter, designed the hotel and it cost more than one million dollars to build in 1929! We walked through the gardens and Mommy and Daddy enjoyed seeing the beautiful antiques and artwork on display.

Next, we stopped to see the "World's Longest Map of U.S. Route 66" that is painted on the side of a building. We had fun pointing to all of the locations where we had already stopped.

Back in the car, we saw a sign for the Meteor Crater. Mommy said we just HAD to stop to see THAT! According to our tour guide, it is believed that a meteorite created the big crater about 50,000 years ago. Looking down into the crater made my knees shake and I held Daddy's hand tighter!

Our next stop was the ghost town of Two Guns. Our guide book said that there was once a zoo and several other attractions here, but all that remains now is what's left of the old buildings. One of them has the words, "MOUNTAIN LIONS" on the front. I was glad they weren't still there!

TWIN ARROWS

Not far down the road was Twin Arrows. Everything here is closed, too, and all that remains are the empty buildings and two huge arrows sticking out of the ground. I wonder how they stay in the ground!

As we entered the Flagstaff area, we saw this really cool guitar sign for the Museum Club. Our guide book said that it was the "southwest's largest log cabin."

We had a yummy lunch at Miz Zip's before stopping at the Flagstaff Visitor's Center. There, we learned that we could drive to Williams, then ride The Grand Canyon Railway to the Grand Canyon.

We were very excited when we finally arrived in Williams. The "wild west" train ride was very exciting, but you'll have to see for yourself what happens on the train!

We all had a very exciting day exploring the Grand Canyon. It is so much larger than any of us had been able to imagine and it was impossible to get it all in one picture.

he Grand Canyon is 277 miles long and up to
3 miles wide. At the bottom of the canyon flows
he Colorado River.

Seligman was our next big stop. Brother Bobby read from our travel guide, "After the interstate bypassed Seligman, no tourists came anymore. The barber, Angel Delgadillo, was afraid Seligman would become a ghost town. He started the Historic Route 66 Association in Arizona so that people would still travel Route 66 in Arizona. Angel's barber shop is now a Visitor's Center." There was so much to see that we stayed all day. We laughed so hard when we saw this funny car beside the Snow Cap Drive-In, where we stopped for ice cream cones. We had dinner at the Roadkill Cafe before continuing our drive towards California.

We passed by more old, abandoned cars.

In Valentine, we stopped at The Keepers of the Wild. It looked like a zoo, but we learned that it is an animal rescue center.

I liked the name of the town of Valentine. There was an old brick building that we learned used to be a Native American school house.

We stopped at the Hackberry General store to get some snacks and look around at all the cool stuff on display.

On Antares Curve, we saw a huge face sculpture and a sign with two aliens waving at us! We all giggled.

Our next stop was in Kingman. We visited the Powerhouse Visitor's Center, which was built in 1909 to supply electric power to the mines, but is now a museum.

The road to Oatman was narrow and winding and Mommy said we all needed to be very quiet while she concentrated on driving. We passed the sign for Sitgreaves Pass and our guide book said that it was 3550 feet high! We felt like we were on top of the world! The view was amazing.

When Mommy suddenly slammed on the brakes, we couldn't believe our eyes when we saw all of the wild burros on the roadway. The car crept along right behind them until we got into Oatman. There were more burros peeking in the shops! We had a lot of fun in this old gold mining town. There was even a wild west show in the street!

We continued on Old Route 66 and soon we were in Needles, California! We found someone to take our picture around this Conestoga Wagon.

The El Garces hotel was being restored. We discovered that it is also owned by the same people who fixed up the La Posado in Winslow and will be just as beautiful when it is done.

Daddy said our next stop would be Cousin Mary and Bob's. We couldn't wait to meet them and tell them all about our trip. I thought about all I had seen and couldn't wait to share my pictures!

We finally arrived at Cousin Mary and Bob's for our visit! Mommy was so happy to see her relatives that she hadn't seen in so long. We stayed for over a week! When we were finally ready to leave, Daddy said we'd have to start heading back home. We wouldn't be able to see the rest of California on this trip. But we had so much fun getting to know Cousins Mary and Bob that we knew we'd be back! I can't wait for our next Route 66 adventure!

Dedications

Anne Maro Slanina

This book is dedicated to all of those who have helped keep The Mother Road alive -- those who own and operate businesses, the people living in the communities and those who travel The Main Street of America. The legacy of the original builders of the spirit of Route 66 is carried through to the present day through the efforts of all of these people. With a heartfelt thank you to all who granted permission for the use of the photographs of their properties and those who have befriended me along the route.

With an extra special thank you to David P. Keppel who worked tirelessly and patiently on the layout of this book while I made up my mind only to change it again-- repeatedly.

And finally, to my mother, whose creativity and sense of wonder has been an inspiration to me.

Kelsey Collins

For my family, especially my mom, for always believing in me and for Mark, I love you.

A Note to Travelers

Please note that the businesses along Route 66, as in all of the country, change constantly. Information was accurate at the time of publication. Please enjoy your trip along the highway, have your own adventure and always watch out for your own safety!

Resources

McClanahan, Jerry. (2008). *Route 66: EZ66 Guide for Travelers:* Second edition. National Historic Route 66 Federation.

National Historic Route 66 Federation. (2008.) *Route 66 Dining & Lodging Guide.*

Ross, Jim; & McClanahan, Jerry. (2005). *Here It Is! The Route 66 Map Series.* Ghost Town Press.

Snyder, Tom. (2000). *Route 66: Traveler's Guide and Roadside Companion.* St. Martin's Griffin.

Wallis, Michael. (2001). Route 66: *The Mother Road 75th Anniversary Edition.* St. Martin's Griffin.

Wickline, David. (2006). *Images of 66: An Interactive Photographic Journey along the Length of the Mother Road.* Roadhouse 66, LLC.